It's Easy To Play Stevie Wonder.

Wise Publications
London/New York/Sydney/Cologne

Exclusive Distributors:
Music Sales Limited
8/9 Frith Street, London W1V 5TZ, England
Music Sales Pty. Limited
27 Clarendon Street, Artarmon, Sydney, NSW 2064, Australia

This book © Copyright 1985 by
Wise Publications
ISBN 0.7119.0707.2
Order No. AM 40007

Art direction by Mike Bell
Cover illustration by Mark Thomas
Arranged by Roger Day
Compiled by Peter Evans

Music Sales complete catalogue lists thousands
of titles and is free from your local music
book shop, or direct from Music Sales Limited.
Please send 50p in stamps for postage to
Music Sales Limited, 8/9 Frith Street, London W1V 5TZ.

I Just Called To Say I Love You

Words and Music by Stevie Wonder

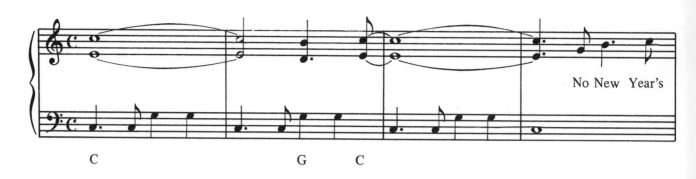

No New Year's

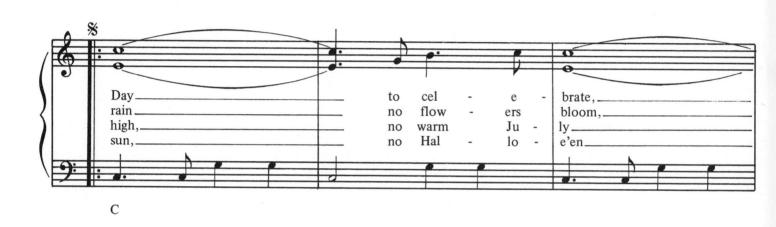

Day to cel - e - brate,
rain no flow - ers bloom,
high, no warm Ju - ly
sun, no Hal - lo - e'en

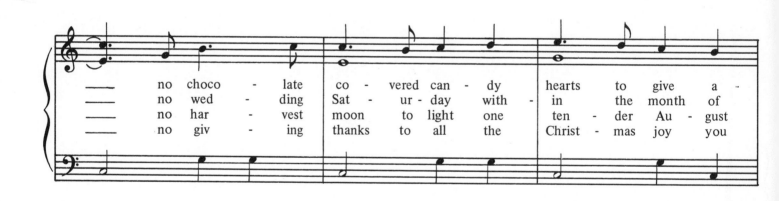

no choco - late co - vered can - dy hearts to give a -
no wed - ding Sat - ur - day with - in the month of
no har - vest moon to light one ten - der Au - gust
no giv - ing thanks to all the Christ - mas joy you

way. No first of spring,
June. But what it is
night. No Au - tumn breeze,
bring. But what it is,

Isn't She Lovely

Words and Music by Stevie Wonder

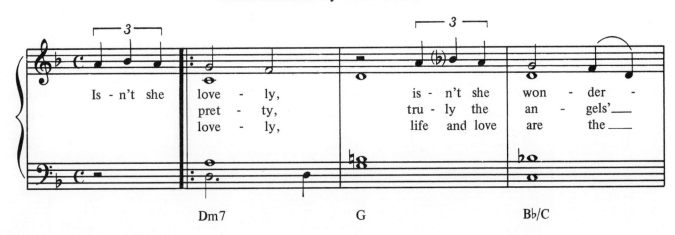

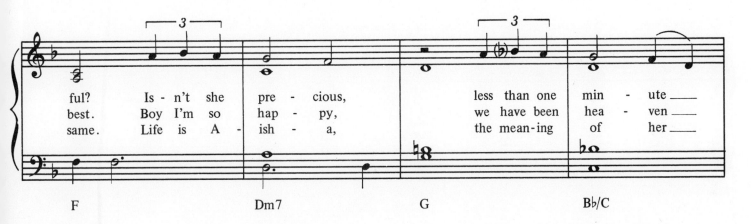

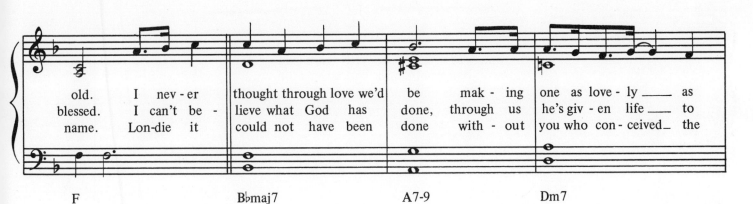

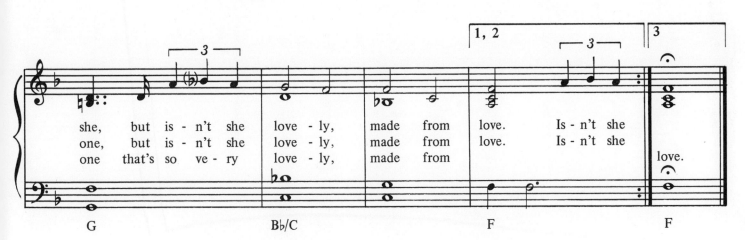

We Can Work It Out

Words and Music by John Lennon and Paul McCartney

Fairly Slow

mp

1. Try to see it my way, Do I have to keep on talk-ing
2. Think of what you're say - ing, You can get it wrong and still you
3. Try to see it my way, On - ly time will tell if I am

G   C   G   C

till I can't go on? While you see it your way.
think that it's all right. Think of what I'm say - ing.
right or I am wrong. While you see it your way.

F   G   C

To Coda ⊕

Run the risk of know-ing that our love may soon be gone.
We can work it out and get it straight or say good-night.
There's a chance that we might fall a - part be-fore too long.

G   C   F   G

We can work it out, We can work it out.____ Life is ve - ry short,

mf

C   G   C   D7   Em

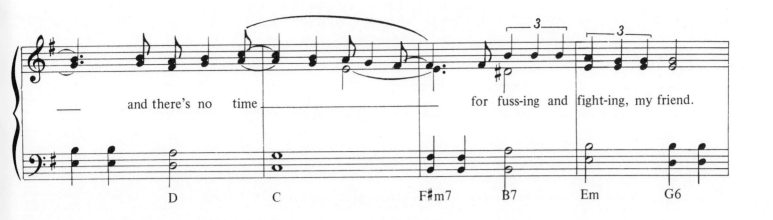

and there's no time   for fuss-ing and fight-ing, my friend.

D   C   F#m7   B7   Em   G6

I have al - ways thought   that it's a crime,

C   Em   D

D.C. al Coda

So I will ask   you once   a - gain.

C   F#m7   B7   Em   G   C   Em

✛ *CODA*

ritard.

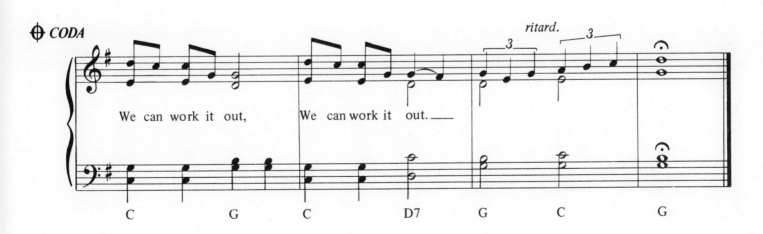

We can work it out,   We can work it out. ___

C   G   C   D7   G   C   G

Superwoman

Words and Music by Stevie Wonder

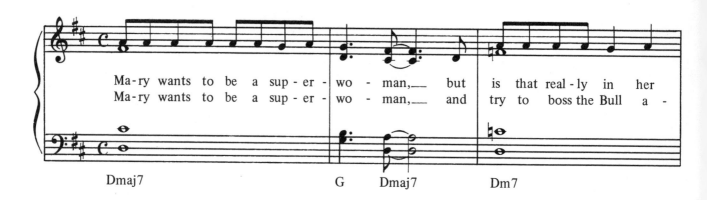

Ma-ry wants to be a sup-er-wo-man,___ but is that real-ly in her
Ma-ry wants to be a sup-er-wo-man,___ and try to boss the Bull a-

Dmaj7   G   Dmaj7   Dm7

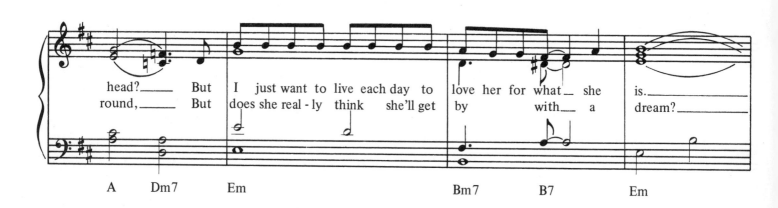

head?___ But I just want to live each day to love her for what___ she is.___
round,___ But does she real-ly think she'll get by with___ a dream?___

A   Dm7   Em   Bm7   B7   Em

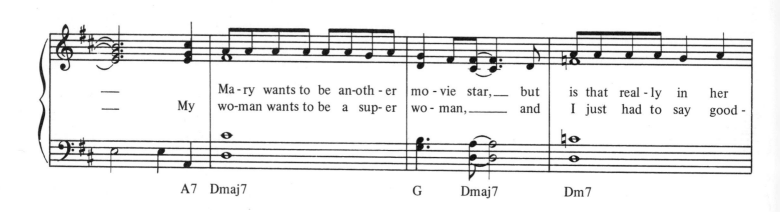

— My Ma-ry wants to be an-oth-er mo-vie star,___ but is that real-ly in her
— wo-man wants to be a sup-er wo-man,___ and I just had to say good-

A7 Dmaj7   G   Dmaj7   Dm7

mind?___ And all the things she wants to be she needs to leave___ be-hind.}
bye.___ Be-cause I can't___ spend all ___ my hours ___ start-ing to cry.}

A7   Dm7   Em   B7   Em

11

I Believe (When I Fall In Love It Will Be Forever)

Words and Music by Stevie Wonder and Yvonne Wright

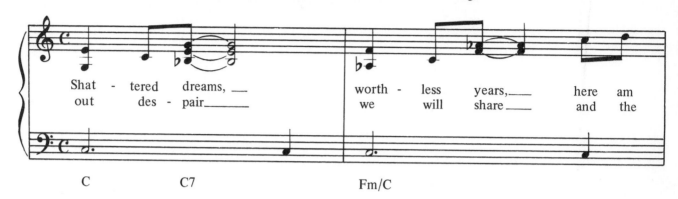

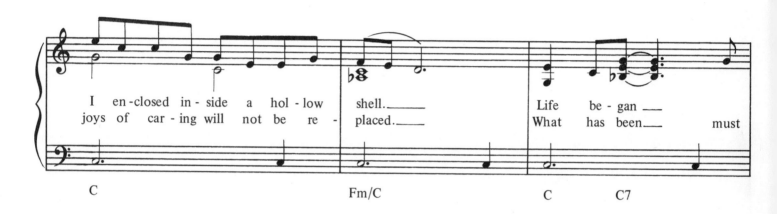

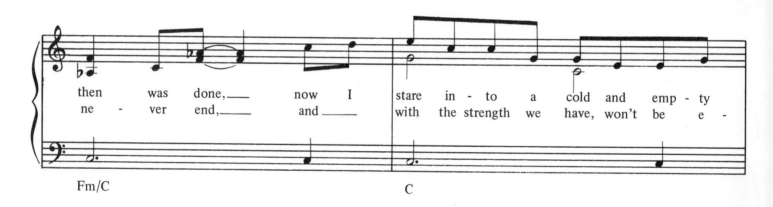

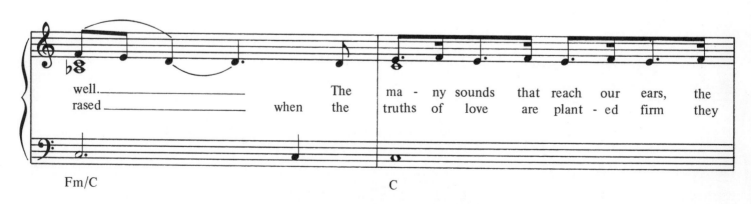

FADE

13

Master Blaster (Jammin')

Words and Music by Stevie Wonder

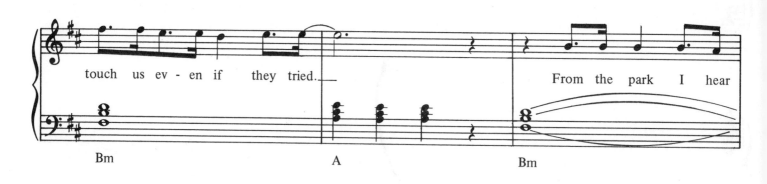

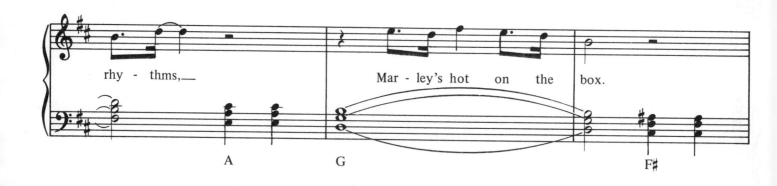

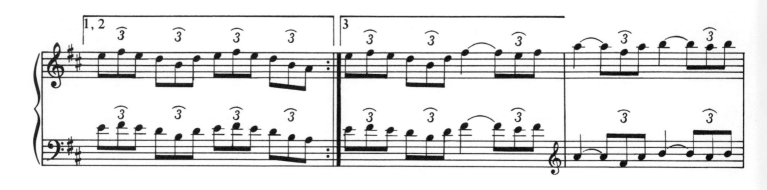

D.S. and FADE

VERSE 2:

They want us to join their fighting.
But our answer today
Is to let all our worries,
Like the breeze, through our fingers, slip away.
Peace has come to Zimbabwe;
Third world's right on the one;
Now's the time for celebration.
'Cause we've only just begun.
Didn't know . . . *(To Chorus)*

VERSE 3:

You ask me am I happy;
Well, as a matter of fact,
I can say that I'm ecstatic,
'Cause we all just made a pact.
We've agreed to get together;
Joined as children in Jah.
When you're moving in the positive,
Your destination is the brightest star.
Didn't know . . . *(To Chorus)*

Chorus: (vocal ad lib)

Oh, oh, oh, oh, oh, you
(We're in the middle of the makin's
Of the master blaster jammin'.)
Would be jammin' until the break of dawn.
Don't you stop the music, oh no.
(We're in the middle of the makin's
Of the master blaster jammin').

(Repeat background)

Oh, oh, oh, you
(We're in the middle of the makin's
Of the master blaster jammin').
Would be jammin' until the break of dawn.
I bet you if some one approached you yesterday
To tell you that you would be jammin',
You would not believe it because
You never thought you would be jammin'.
Oh, oh, oh, oh,
(We're in the middle of the makin's
Of the master blaster jammin').
Jammin' til the break of dawn.
Oh, oh, oh, you may as well believe
What you're feeling because you feel your body jammin'.
Oh, oh, you would be jammin' until the break of dawn.
(We're in the middle of the makin's
Of the master blaster jammin').

(Repeat background)

16

Knocks Me Off My Feet

Words and Music by Stevie Wonder

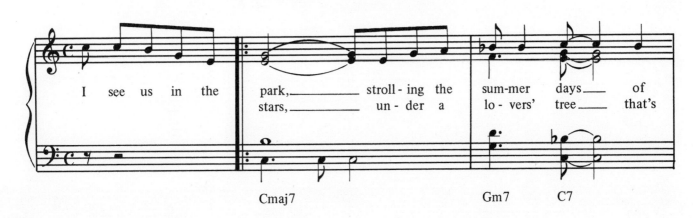

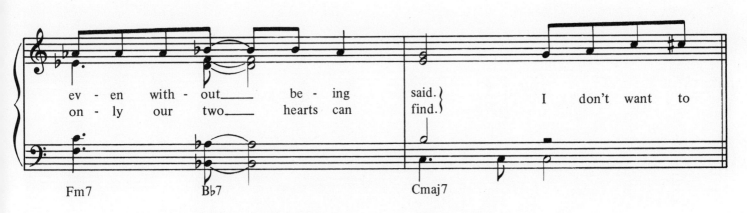

Repeat to FADE

You And I

Words and Music by Stevie Wonder

Verse 2: Will it stay, the love you feel for me?
Will it say that you will be by my side to see me through;
Until my life is through?
(To Chorus:)

Verse 3: I am glad, at least in my life,
I found someone that may not be here forever to see me through;
But I found strength in you.

Verse 4: I only pray that I have shown you
A brighter day, because that's all that I am living for, you see;
Don't worry what happens to me.
(To Chorus:)

Blame It On The Sun

Words and Music by Stevie Wonder and Syreeta Wright

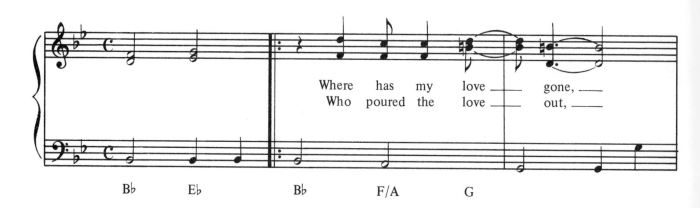

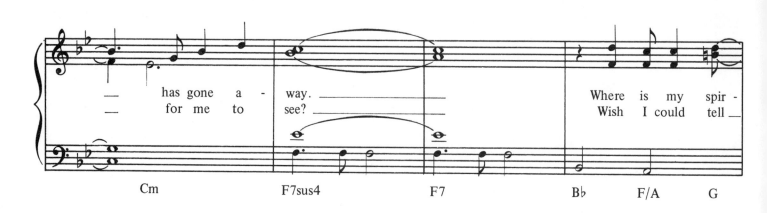

All In Love Is Fair

Words and Music by Stevie Wonder

Boogie On Reggae Woman

Words and Music by Stevie Wonder

Higher Ground

Words and Music by Stevie Wonder

Additional Lyrics: *(Repeat last 4 bars as written-sing additional lyrics below)*

Don't you let nobody bring you down. They'll sho' nuff try.
God is gonna show you Higher Ground. He's the only friend you have around.

Superstition

Words and Music by Stevie Wonder

You Haven't Done Nothin'

Words and Music by Stevie Wonder

Don't You Worry 'Bout A Thing

Words and Music by Stevie Wonder

Moderate Latin Rhythm

3. Ba - bum - ba - bum - ba - bum, ba - bum.
   Bum, bum, bum, bum, bum, bum, bum.

4. Ev'rybody needs a change, a chance to check out the new.
   But you're the only one to see, the changes you take yourself through.
   Don't you worry 'bout a thing. Don't you worry 'bout a thing, pretty mama,
   'Cause I'll be standin' in the wings when you check it out.

You Are The Sunshine Of My Life

Words and Music by Stevie Wonder

Moderately, with feeling

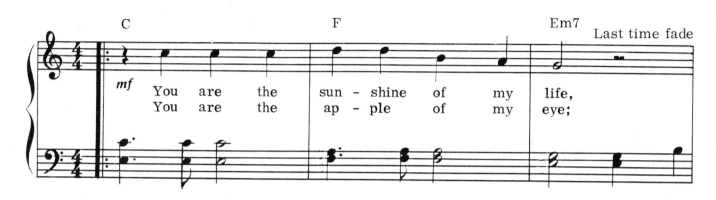

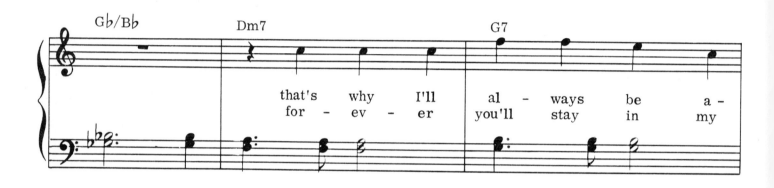

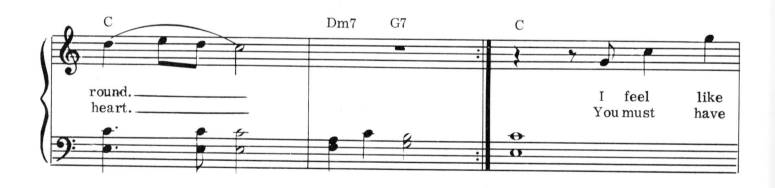

C   F   E7

'though I've loved you for a mil - lion years.
be - cause you came to my res - cue.

A   D E

And if I thought our love was
And I know that this must be

Am   D7

end - ing,___ I'd ___ find my - self
heav - en; ___ how could so much love

G G7   D. C.

drown-ing in my ___ own tears. Whoa. ___
be in - side ___ of you? Whoa. ___

I Wish

Words and Music by Stevie Wonder

would not get a thing, we were hap - py with the joy the day would bring. Sneak - in' out ____ the back door to hang - out with those hood - lum friends of mine. ____ Ooh, _____ greet - ed at ____ the back door ___ with, "Boy, I thought I told ____ you not to go out - side." ____

To Coda ✛

46

so.   Do   do   do   do   do   do   do   do   do   do   do   do,

do   do   do   do   do   do   do   do   do   do   do   do.

D.S. al Coda

Coda

(so.)

Repeat and Fade

Brother says he's tellin'
'Bout you playin' doctor with that girl
Just don't tell, I'll give you
Anything you want in this whole wide world.
Mama gives you money for Sunday school
You trade yours for candy after church is through.

Smokin' cigarettes and writing something nasty on the wall (you nasty boy).
Teacher sends you to the principal's office down the hall.
You grow up and learn that kinda thing ain't right
But while you were doin' it – it sure felt outta sight.

I wish those days could come back once more.
Why did those days ev--er have to go?
I wish those days could come back once more.
Why did those days ev--er have to go?
'Cause I loved them so.

Reproduced and printed by Halstan & Co. Ltd., Amersham, Bucks., England

Checklist of important piano books.

The books below are available from your local music shop
who will order them for you if not in stock.
If there is no music shop near you, you may order direct from
Music Sales Limited (Dept. M), 8/9 Frith Street, London W1V 5TZ
Please always include 85p to cover post/packing costs.

A Start At The Piano
AM 40650

**Alison Bell's Graded
For Piano Pieces
Book 1: Very Easy**
AM 30297

**Book 5: Upper
Intermediate**
AM 30339

**Anthology Of Piano
Music Volume 1:
Baroque**
AM 10968

Volume 3: Romantic
AM 10984

**Barrelhouse And Boog
Piano**
OK 64659

**Big Note Piano
Book 1**
AM 28226

**Bud Powell: Jazz
Masters Series**
AM 23219

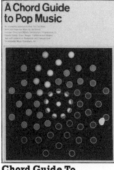

**Chord Guide To
Pop Music**
AM 10596

**The Classic Piano
Repertoire Bach**
EW 50023

Chopin
EW 50015

**Promenade Theory
Papers Book 1**
PB 40583

**Classics To Moderns
Book 1**
YK 20014

**Classics To Moderns
Sonatas & Sonatinas**
YK 20204

Themes & Variations
YK 20196

**More Classics To
Moderns Book 1**
YK 20121

**Dave Brubeck: Jazz
Masters Series**
AM 21189

**Easy Classical Piano
Duets**
AM 31949

**The Complete Piano
Player By Kenneth
Baker Book 1**
AM 34828

Book 2
AM 34836

Book 3
AM 34844

Book 4
AM 34851

Book 5
AM 34869

Style Book
AM 35338